KT-420-411

PRACTICE PAPERS FOR HIGHER MATHEMATICS

Units 1, 2 & 3

by

P.W. Westwood,
Principal Teacher of Mathematics,
Kirkcaldy High School

ISBN 0 7169 8019 3
© P.W. Westwood 2002

ROBERT GIBSON · Publisher
17 Fitzroy Place, Glasgow, G3 7SF, Scotland, U.K.
www.gibson-books.co.uk

PREFACE

These practice examination papers were devised by the author to give candidates sitting the National Qualifications Higher Level Mathematics Examination extra practice with working through exam papers. This is a popular and useful way of preparing for the exam and it can be useful to set yourself 1 hour 10 minutes for Paper 1 and 1 hour 30 minutes for Paper 2. You can then revise a particular type of question by referring to the question analysis table at the back of this book.

COPYING PROHIBITED

Note: This publication is NOT licensed for copying under the Copyright Licensing Agency's Scheme, to which Robert Gibson & Sons are not party.

All rights reserved. No part of this publication may be reproduced; stored in a retrieval system; or transmitted in any form or by any means — electronic, mechanical, photocopying, or otherwise — without prior permission of the publisher Robert Gibson & Sons, Ltd., 17 Fitzroy Place, Glasgow, G3 7SF.

MATHEMATICS

HIGHER GRADE

INSTRUCTIONS TO CANDIDATES

Paper 1 — Non-calculator

Time: 1 hour 10 minutes

1. **Calculators may <u>not</u> be used in this paper**.

2. Full credit will be given only where the solution contains appropriate working.

3. Answers obtained by readings from scale drawings will not receive any credit.

Paper 2

Time: 1 hour 30 minutes

1. **Calculators may be used in this paper**.

2. Full credit will be given only where the solution contains appropriate working.

3. Answers obtained by readings from scale drawings will not receive any credit.

FORMULAE LIST

Circle:

The equation $x^2 + y^2 + 2gx + 2fy + c = 0$ represents a circle centre $(-g, -f)$ and radius $\sqrt{g^2 + f^2 - c}$.

The equation $(x - a)^2 + (y - b)^2 = r^2$ represents a circle centre (a, b) and radius r.

Scalar Product:

$\boldsymbol{a}.\boldsymbol{b} = |\boldsymbol{a}|\,|\boldsymbol{b}| \cos \theta$, where θ is the angle between $\boldsymbol{a}$ and $\boldsymbol{b}$

or $\qquad \boldsymbol{a}.\boldsymbol{b} = a_1b_1 + a_2b_2 + a_3b_3$ where $\boldsymbol{a} = \begin{pmatrix} a_1 \\ a_2 \\ a_3 \end{pmatrix}$ and $\boldsymbol{b} = \begin{pmatrix} b_1 \\ b_2 \\ b_3 \end{pmatrix}$

Trigonometric formulae:

$$\sin (A \pm B) = \sin A \cos B \pm \cos A \sin B$$
$$\cos (A \pm B) = \cos A \cos B \mp \sin A \sin B$$
$$\sin 2A = 2\sin A \cos A$$
$$\cos 2A = \cos^2 A - \sin^2 A = 2\cos^2 A - 1 = 1 - 2\sin^2 A$$

Table of standard derivatives and integrals:

$f(x)$	$f'(x)$
$\sin ax$	$a \cos ax$
$\cos ax$	$-a \sin ax$

$f(x)$	$\int f(x)$
$\sin ax$	$-\dfrac{1}{a} \cos ax + C$
$\cos ax$	$\dfrac{1}{a} \sin ax + C$

PRACTICE PAPER A

MATHEMATICS
HIGHER
Paper 1
(Non-calculator)

Refer to page 3 for Instructions to Candidates

All questions should be attempted

Marks

1. The points P and Q have coordinates $(p, 2p^2)$ and $(2q, 8q^2)$ respectively.

   Determine the gradient of PQ in its simplest form. **(2)**

2. A sequence is defined by the recurrence relation $u_{n+1} = k u_n + 6$.

   (a) If $k = 0.4$, find the limit of the sequence as $n \to \infty$. **(2)**

   (b) Find the value of k for which the limit of the sequence is 18. **(2)**

3. If $\sin \theta = \frac{3}{5}$, $0 < \theta < \frac{\pi}{2}$, find the **exact** value of

   (a) $\cos 2\theta$, **(2)**

   (b) $\cos 4\theta$. **(2)**

Marks

4. Write down the equation of the circle which

   (a) has centre (1, 2) and passes through the origin, **(2)**

   (b) has centre (3, 4) and touches the *x*-axis. **(2)**

5. Show that the equation $(k + 1)x^2 + (3k + 2)x + (2k + 1) = 0$ has real roots for all real values of *k*.

   (4)

6. If $y = \sin^3 x$, find $\dfrac{dy}{dx}$. **(3)**

7. The graph of $y = f(x)$ is shown.

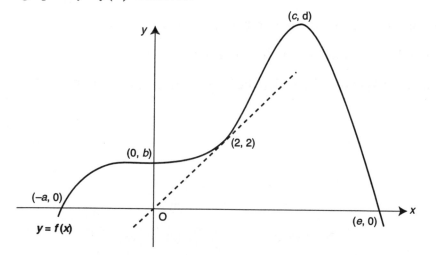

- It cuts the *x*-axis at (−*a*, 0) and (*e*, 0).
- There is a rising point of inflection at (0, *b*).
- There is a maximum turning point at (*c*, *d*).
- The equation of the tangent at the point (2, 2) is $y = x$.

Sketch the graph of $y = f'(x)$, showing as much information as you can. **(4)**

8. In order to enhance the corporate image of his establishment, the hotelier of the Avoch Arms has designed this new logo.

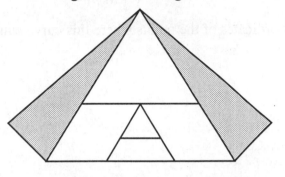

The shape consists of an isosceles triangle PQS, two congruent right-angled triangles PTS and QRS, with $T\hat{S}R$ also a right angle.

QR = 8 cm and SR = 15 cm and $Q\hat{S}R = x°$.

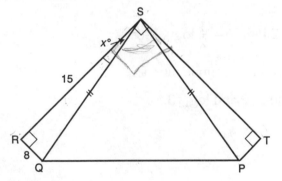

(a) Find the length QS. **(1)**

(b) Express the size of $P\hat{S}Q$ in terms of $x°$. **(1)**

(c) Show that the exact value of sin $P\hat{S}Q$ is $\dfrac{161}{289}$ **(4)**

(d) Calculate the area of the logo (i.e., the pentagon PQRST). **(3)**

Marks

9. *(a)* Sketch the graph of $y = 1 + 2 \cos\left(x + \dfrac{\pi}{6}\right)$ for $0 \le x \le 2\pi$. **(3)**

   (b) Find the coordinates of the points where this curve cuts the x- and y-axes. **(4)**

10. Evaluate $\displaystyle\int_1^2 \sqrt{3x - 2}\, dx$ **(4)**

11. Express $\log_{10} 5 + 2 \log_{10} 6 - \dfrac{1}{2} \log_{10} 100$

   (a) as the logarithm of a single number, **(3)**

   (b) in terms of $\log_{10} 2$ and $\log_{10} 3$. **(2)**

Total: 50 marks

[END OF QUESTION PAPER]

NATIONAL
QUALIFICATIONS
Time 1 hour 30 minutes

PRACTICE PAPER A

MATHEMATICS
HIGHER
Paper 2

Refer to page 3 for Instructions to Candidates

All questions should be attempted

Marks

1. Given that $a = 2i - 3j + k$, $b = i + 3j - 4k$ and $c = 4i - j + tk$, find the value of t for which c is perpendicular to $a - b$. **(4)**

2. A small marquee is in the shape of a cuboid surmounted by a pyramid. The cuboid and the pyramid have equal heights.

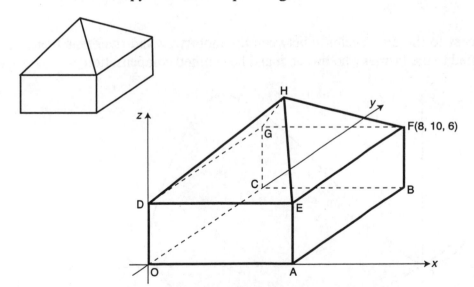

If axes are taken as shown, F has coordinates (8, 10, 6).

   (a) Write down the coordinates of B, D and H. **(3)**

   (b) Calculate the size of DĤB. **(7)**

Marks

3. *(a)* Show that the point A(-1, -3) lies on the circle with equation $x^2 + y^2 - 6x + 8y + 8 = 0$. **(1)**

    (b) Find the equation of the tangent at A to this circle. **(4)**

    (c) Show that this line is also a tangent to the parabola with equation $y = x^2 + 5$, stating the coordinates of the point of contact. **(6)**

4. Express $2 \sin x° - \sqrt{5} \cos x°$ in the form $k \sin(x - \alpha)°$ where $k > 0$ and $0 \leq \alpha \leq 360$. **(4)**

5. Part of a river can be represented (relative to suitable axes) by the equation $y = \frac{1}{5}x^2(5 - x)$.

    A sweeping bend of a motorway was built to follow a path represented by $y = \frac{1}{5}x(x - 5)$.

    Access to the area enclosed between the motorway and river was then denied to the farmer who owned it and he claimed compensation.

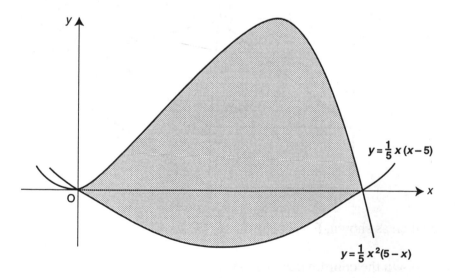

    Calculate the area of the ground he lost. **(6)**

Marks

6.   *(a)*   The function f is defined by $f(x) = x^3 - 2x^2 - 5x + 6$.

           The function g is defined by $g(x) = x - 1$.

           Show that $f(g(x)) = x^3 - 5x^2 + 2x + 8$.   **(4)**

     (b)   Factorise fully $f(g(x))$.   **(3)**

     (c)   The function k is such that $k(x) = \dfrac{1}{f(g(x))}$.

           For what values of x is the function k not defined?   **(2)**

7.   Ravenscraig Zoo is looking for a new venue.

     One suggestion included in the proposed move is to build the new aviary up against the outer wall of the giraffe house as shown.

     The height of the aviary is to be 4 metres, and its volume is to be 800 m³.

     Take the length and breadth of the base to be y metres and x metres respectively as shown.

     The material for the walls costs £3 per square metre and that for the roof £2 per square metre.

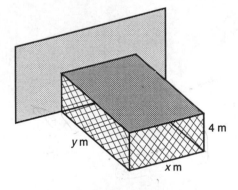

     (a)   Show that the cost £C of material is given by

$$C = 400 + 12x + \frac{4800}{x}$$ **(5)**

     (b)   Find the dimensions of the aviary which will keep the expenditure on material to a minimum, and calculate this minimum cost.   **(7)**

Marks

8. If $y = 100\,x^4$, prove that the graph of $\log_{10} y$ against $\log_{10} x$ is a straight line, giving its equation in its simplest form. **(4)**

Total: 60 marks

[END OF QUESTION PAPER]

NATIONAL
QUALIFICATIONS
Time 1 hour 10 minutes

PRACTICE PAPER B

MATHEMATICS
HIGHER
Paper 1
(Non-calculator)

Refer to page 3 for Instructions to Candidates

All questions should be attempted

Marks

1. $\triangle ABC$ has vertices A(–1, 2), B(5, 4) and C(7, 2).

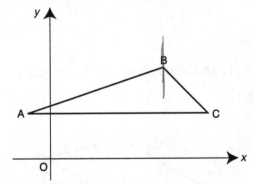

   Write down the equation of the altitude which passes through B. **(1)**

2. Find the equation of the circle which passes through the origin, 6 on the *y*-axis and 8 on the *x*-axis.

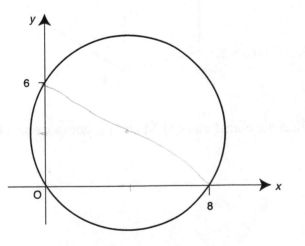

(3)

13

3. Show that $(x + 1)$ is a factor of $f(x) = 2x^3 - 5x^2 - x + 6$ and hence factorise $f(x)$ completely.

(4)

4. The function f is defined by $f(x) = 5 + 4x - x^2$.

    (a)   Express $f(x)$ in the form $a + b(x + c)^2$.

(3)

    (b)   For what range of values of x is $f(x)$ both negative and increasing?

(3)

5. ABCD,EFGH is a cuboid.

The coordinates of A, B, D and H are shown in the diagram.

M is the midpoint of HG.

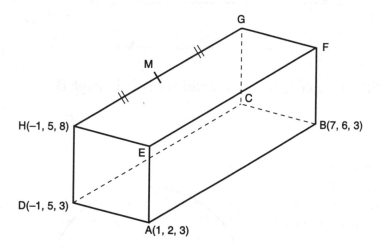

Find the coordinates of M and the components of $\overrightarrow{AM}$.

(4)

Marks

6. If $f(x) = \dfrac{x^2 + 1}{\sqrt{x}}$, evaluate $f'(4)$. **(5)**

7. The graph of the cubic function with equation $y = f(x)$ is shown.

It cuts the x-axis at the points $(-a, 0)$, $(b, 0)$ and $(e, 0)$.

There is a maximum turning point at $(0, 2)$ and a minimum turning point at $(c, -d)$.

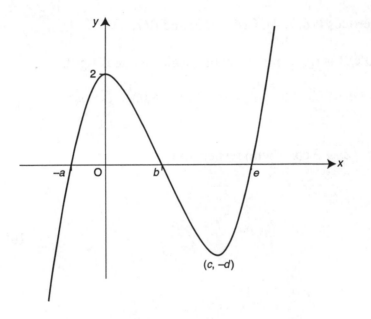

(a) Make a copy of this diagram and on it sketch the graph of $y = 4 - f(x)$, indicating the coordinates of the turning points. **(4)**

(b) On a separate diagram, sketch the graph of $y = f'(x)$. **(2)**

Marks

8. Solve $2 \sin 2x + 1 = 0$ for $0 \le x \le 2\pi$. (4)

9. By expressing $\cos x - \sin x$ as a single trigonometrical function, find its maximum value and the value of x between 0 and 2π for which it occurs. (6)

10. Given $y = \sqrt[3]{x} - \dfrac{1}{\sqrt[4]{x}}$ find $\int y \, dx$. (4)

11. $\triangle PQR$ has vertices P(6, 2, 4), Q(4, –2, 5) and R(7, –3, 7).

    Prove that $\triangle PQR$ is right angled, stating which angle is right. (4)

12. Differentiate $\sqrt{2x + 3\cos x}$ with respect to x. (3)

Total: 50 marks

[END OF QUESTION PAPER]

NATIONAL
QUALIFICATIONS
Time 1 hour 30 minutes

PRACTICE PAPER B

MATHEMATICS
HIGHER
Paper 2

Refer to page 3 for Instructions to Candidates

All questions should be attempted

Marks

1. A sequence is defined by the recurrence relation
$$u_{n+1} = 1{\cdot}5u_n + 5 \text{ and } u_0 = 5.$$

   Find *(a)*   the values of u_1, u_2 and u_3,   **(2)**

         (b)   which term of the sequence is the first to exceed 1000.   **(2)**

2. Triangle PQR has vertices P(–9, 5), Q(10, 3) and R(1, –15).

   Find *(a)*   the equation of the altitude PS,   **(3)**

         (b)   the equation of the median QT,   **(3)**

   and *(c)*   the coordinates of V, the point of intersection of PS and QT.   **(4)**

3. Find where the line with equation $x + 2y = 15$ meets the circle with equation $x^2 + y^2 = 50$, and hence find the length of the chord joining these points.   **(7)**

4. *(a)*   Show that $3\cos 2x° + \cos x° + 1$ can be written as
$$6\cos^2 x° + \cos x° - 2.$$
           (1)

   (b)   Hence solve $3\cos 2x° + \cos x° + 1 = 0$ for $0 \le x \le 360$.   **(4)**

17

Marks

5. This diagram shows the graph of the function $y = a + b \cos cx$ for $0 \le x \le \pi$.

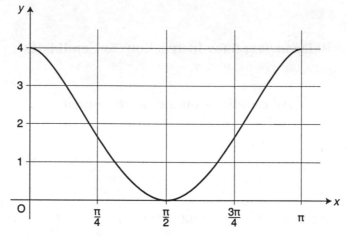

(a) Write down the values of a, b and c. **(3)**

(b) Find, correct to three decimal places, the values of x for which $y = 1.5$. *need to work in radians* **(4)**

6. The cross section of a room looks like this.

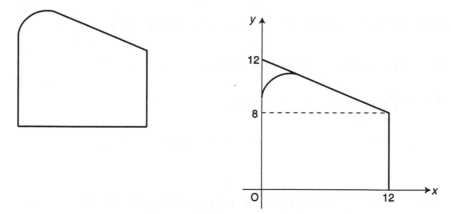

With axes taken as shown, the rafters are seen to run from the point $(0, 12)$ to the point $(12, 8)$.

(a) Find the equation of the rafters. **(2)**

The equation of the curved part of the ceiling is $6y = 63 + 4x - x^2$.

(b) Show that the rafters are tangential to the curved part of the ceiling, identifying the coordinates of the point of contact. **(6)**

18

Marks

✗ **7.** Given that $|p| = 4$ and $p.q = 8$, show that p is perpendicular to $(p - 2q)$. **(4)**

✗ **8.** The base of a 10 m tall lighting mast is 3 m away from the junction box, as shown.

A connecting cable has to be run from the top of the mast to the junction box, without (for some reason) going underground, so it comes part way down the mast and then through the air to the junction box.

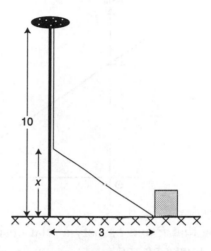

A protective cover for the cable costs £1 per metre where the cable is in contact with the mast and £2 per metre where it is passing through the air (because it needs covered all round).

(a) If the point where the cable leaves the mast to pass through the air is x metres above the base of the mast, show that the cost, £C, of the protective cover is given by $C = 10 - x + 2(9 + x^2)^{1/2}$. **(2)**

(b) Find the value of x for which this cost is a minimum. **(7)**

Marks

9. In an experiment to establish the relationship between two quantities P and t, the values of $\log_e P$ were plotted against those of $\log_e t$, and the following graph obtained.

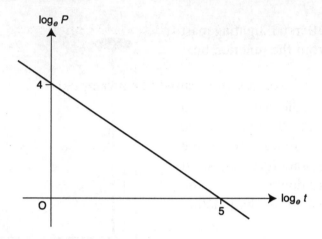

Show that P and t satisfy a relationship of the form $P = kt^r$, calculating the values of k and r.

(6)

Total: 60 marks

[END OF QUESTION PAPER]

NATIONAL
QUALIFICATIONS
Time 1 hour 10 minutes

PRACTICE PAPER C

MATHEMATICS
HIGHER
Paper 1
(Non-calculator)

Refer to page 3 for Instructions to Candidates

All questions should be attempted

Marks

1. In $\triangle ABC$, A is the point $(-1, 3)$, B$(-2, -3)$ and C$(3, 1)$.

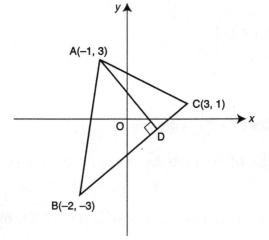

   Find the equation of the altitude AD.　　　　　　　　　　　　　　　(3)

2. Calculate the length of the vector $i + 2j - 2k$.　　　　　　　　　　(2)

3. Find the value of t for which u and v are perpendicular, where
   $u = 2i - j + 3k$ and $v = 2i + tj + 4k$.　　　　　　　　　　　　(3)

Marks

4. The graph, shown, of $y = f(x)$ has a maximum turning point at (b, c), a point of inflection at $(0, d)$ and a minimum turning point at (f, g).

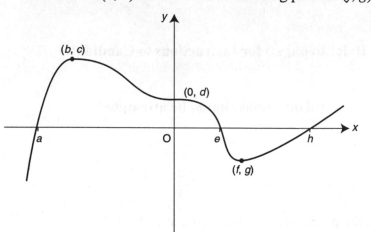

Sketch the graph of $y = f'(x)$. **(4)**

5. Given $f(x) = 3 + 2\cos\left(x + \dfrac{\pi}{3}\right)$, write down

    (a) the greatest value of $f(x)$ and the value of x, $0 \le x \le 2\pi$, for which it occurs, **(2)**

    (b) the least value of $f(x)$ and the value of x, $0 \le x \le 2\pi$, for which it occurs. **(2)**

6. The points P(–1, –2) and Q(3, 8) are the ends of a diameter of a circle.

    Find *(a)* the equation of the circle, **(3)**

        (b) the equation of the tangent to this circle at Q. **(3)**

Marks

7. My cat gets put out every night, and I put her food (250 g of Purrphect) in her dish every morning before I let her in.

   Every day she eats only 80% of whatever amount of food is originally in her dish in the morning.

   If the dish holds 350 g of Purrphect when full, will it ever overflow if this feeding pattern is maintained indefinitely? **(6)**

8. Evaluate $\log_3 243$ exactly. **(2)**

9. Prove that $y = 4x - 9$ is a tangent to the curve $y = 4x(x - 2)$ and find the coordinates of the point of contact. **(5)**

10. In $\triangle PQR$, the altitude RS is 15 cm long.

    PS = 20 cm and SQ = 8 cm.

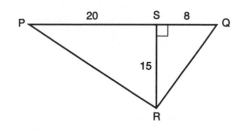

    Find the exact value of $\sin P\hat{R}Q$, and hence estimate the size of $P\hat{R}Q$ (in degrees), giving a reason for your estimate. **(6)**

11. Given that $f(t) = (1 - 3t)^4$, evaluate $f'\left(\dfrac{1}{6}\right)$.   **(3)**

12. Evaluate $\displaystyle\int_{\pi/9}^{\pi/3} 2\cos\left(3x - \dfrac{\pi}{3}\right) dx$ **(3)**

13. Solve for x: $\log_3(x + 1) - \log_3(x - 1) = 2$.   **(3)**

Total: 50 marks

[END OF QUESTION PAPER]

NATIONAL
QUALIFICATIONS
Time 1 hour 30 minutes

PRACTICE PAPER C

MATHEMATICS
HIGHER
Paper 2

Refer to page 3 for Instructions to Candidates

All questions should be attempted

Marks

1.   Differentiate $(3x + 4)^5$ with respect to x.   **(2)**

2.   The functions f and g are defined on suitable domains by $f(x) = \cos x$ and $g(x) = 1 - x^2$.

Find and simplify the formulae for

(i) $g(f(x))$,

(ii) $g(g(x))$.   **(5)**

3.   The diagram shows a cuboid which is 8 cm by 6 cm by 4 cm.

Calculate the angle between the space diagonal AG and the base ABCD.

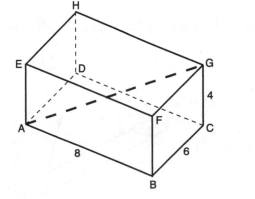

(4)

4.   Solve the equation $x^3 - 4x^2 + x + 6 = 0$.   **(5)**

Marks

5. A silversmith has designed an earring which is bounded by a semicircle and a parabola as shown.

Relative to appropriate axes, the parabola has equation $y = x^2 - 4$.

Calculate the area of the earring.

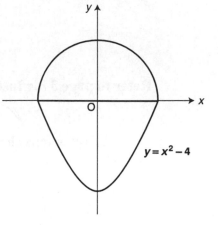

(5)

6. In a fantasy computer game, three tubes arrive at A from P, Q and R as shown.

Relative to suitable axes, P is (5, 6, 8), Q(6, 11, 5), R(10, –1, –5) and A(3, 7, 6).

(a) Show that the three tubes are mutually perpendicular (i.e., any two of the three are at right angles).

(4)

(b) If B is the point (5, 8, 9), calculate the size of $\hat{\text{PAB}}$.

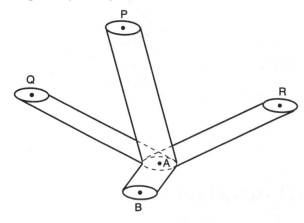

(6)

26

Marks

7.   A curve has equation $y = x^3 - 2x^2 - 3x + 1$.

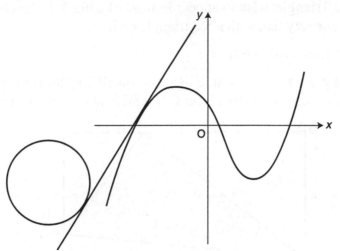

(a)   Find the equation of the tangent to the curve at the point $(-1, 1)$, and show that it passes through the point $(0, 5)$ with gradient 4.   **(5)**

(b)   Show that this line is also a tangent to the circle with equation $x^2 + y^2 + 12x + 4y + 23 = 0$, stating the point of contact.   **(5)**

8.   The diagram shows part of the graph of $f(x) = \log_4 x$.

Sketch the graph of $f'(x)$.

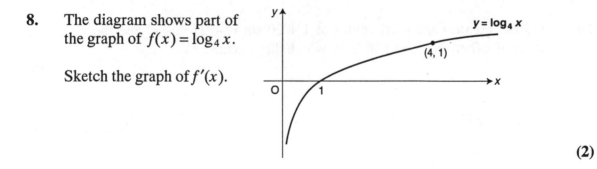

(2)

Marks

9. For their appearance on *Top of the Pops*, the heavy metal combo 'The Temperence Triangle' wish to appear in front of a black 10 feet by 8 feet rectangular scenery flat, with a red triangle on it.

   The triangle is created as follows:

   In the rectangle ABCD, a point E is taken on BC, x feet from B, and a point F is taken on CD, $3x$ feet from C. △AFE is to be painted red.

   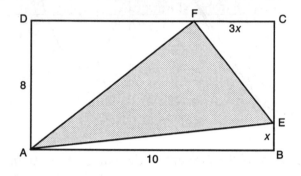

   (a) Show that the area, A square feet, of the red triangle is given by
   $$A = 40 - 5x + \frac{3}{2}x^2.$$
   (3)

   (b) Find the least possible area for the red triangle. (6)

10. Find the greatest and least values of $1 + 20 \sin x° - 21 \cos x°$ and the values of x (between 0 and 360) for which they occur.

    (8)

Total: 60 marks

[END OF QUESTION PAPER]

NATIONAL
QUALIFICATIONS
Time 1 hour 10 minutes

PRACTICE PAPER D

MATHEMATICS
HIGHER
Paper 1
(Non-calculator)

Refer to page 3 for Instructions to Candidates

All questions should be attempted

Marks

1. A is the point $(1, 3)$ and $B(5, -7)$.

    Find the equation of the perpendicular bisector of AB. **(4)**

2. Find the equation of the tangent to the curve $y = 4\sqrt{x}$ at the point where $x = 1$. **(5)**

3. Find the equation of the circle which has centre $(5, 2)$ and which touches the y-axis. **(2)**

4. Express $1 - 6x - x^2$ in the form $a - (x + b)^2$. **(3)**

5. V,ABCD is a right rectangular pyramid, placed relative to coordinate axes so that

$$\overrightarrow{AB} = 4i - 8j + 2k, \quad \overrightarrow{AD} = 6i + 2j - 4k \text{ and } \overrightarrow{AV} = 10i + 2j + 9k.$$

X is the centre of the base ABCD and L is the point $\frac{4}{5}$ of the way up XV.

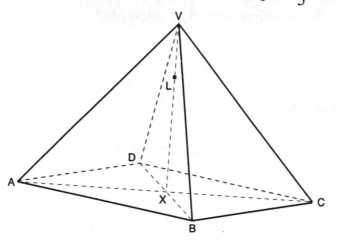

Find the components of

(a) $\overrightarrow{CX}$ (3)

(b) $\overrightarrow{XV}$ (2)

(c) $\overrightarrow{CL}$ (3)

6. Calculate the area of the shaded region.

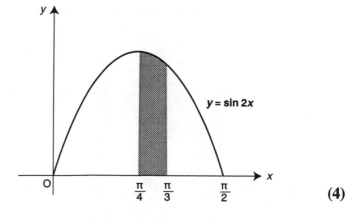

$y = \sin 2x$

(4)

Marks

7. Part of the graph of the cubic function with equation $y = f(x)$ is shown in this diagram.

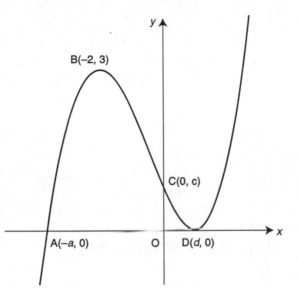

Make two separate copies of this diagram and use them to sketch the graphs of

(a) $y = f(x - 2)$, **(2)**

(b) $y = -f(x) + 3$, **(3)**

indicating on each graph the images of A, B, C and D.

8. (a)   The graph of $y = x^3 + kx^2 + x - 4$ passes through the point $(1, 0)$. Find the value of k. **(2)**

(b)   Prove that this graph does not cross the x-axis at any other point. **(4)**

9. Express $\sqrt{3} \cos x + \sin x$ in the form $R \cos (x - \alpha)$ where $r > 0$ and $0 < \alpha < 2\pi$. **(4)**

10. For $f(x) = \sin 2x - \cos 4x$, find the exact value of $f'\left(\dfrac{\pi}{3}\right)$. **(4)**

11. Solve $\cos 2x - \cos x + 1 = 0$ for $0 \le x \le 2\pi$. **(5)**

Total: 50 marks

[END OF QUESTION PAPER]

NATIONAL
QUALIFICATIONS
Time 1 hour 30 minutes

PRACTICE PAPER D

MATHEMATICS
HIGHER
Paper 2

Refer to page 3 for Instructions to Candidates

All questions should be attempted

Marks

1. △ABC has vertices A(−16, −7), B(12, −3) and C(7, 7).

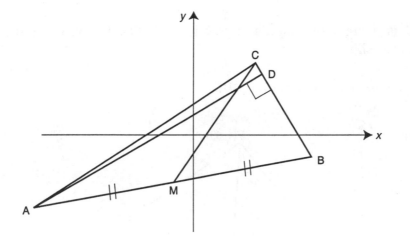

   Find *(a)*   the equation of the median CM,   **(3)**

         (b)   the equation of the altitude AD,   **(3)**

         (c)   the coordinates of the point of intersection of CM and AD.   **(4)**

2. Write down the coordinates of the centre of the circle with equation $x^2 + y^2 + 6x - 6y + c = 0$, and find the value of c for which the circle touches both coordinate axes.   **(3)**

Marks

3. Calculate the area of the shaded region shown.

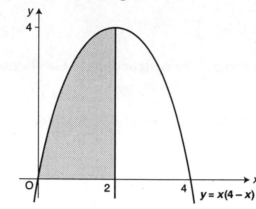

(3)

4. V,OABC is a right rectangular pyramid with OABC lying in the (x, y)-plane as shown.

The vertex V has coordinates (4, 6, 10).

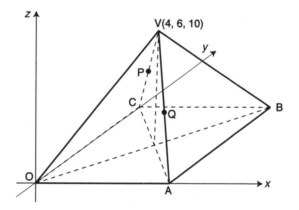

(a) Write down the coordinates of A and C. (2)

(b) Write down the coordinates of P and Q, the mid-points of VC and VA respectively. (2)

(c) Calculate the size of $\hat{POQ}$. (5)

Marks

5. Solve the equation $2 \sin 2x° + 3 \sin x° = 0, 0 \leq x \leq 360$. **(5)**

6. Find $\displaystyle\int \frac{dx}{x\sqrt{x}}$. **(4)**

7. Express $2 + \log_a 3$ as a single logarithm. **(2)**

8. It is known that when a hospital patient has the drug pqβ in the bloodstream, in an hour the body loses 20% of the drug that was in the body at the start of the hour.

    (a) Show that 4 hours after an injection of pqβ, a patient will have lost about 60% of the dose that was administered. **(3)**

    (b) Patient X is being given a 250 mg injection of pqβ every 4 hours. The drug is only effective once the level of it in the bloodstream is continuously above 150 mg. After how many injections is the drug effective? **(3)**

    (c) If the level of the drug in the body exceeds 500 mg, brain damage can result. Is it safe to continue with these injections indefinitely? **(5)**

9. Given that $P = 4Q + 1·1$, where $P = \log_e p$ and $Q = \log_e q$, express p in terms of q. **(4)**

Marks

10. A new trophy has been designed for the pupil with the best score in the Higher Mathematics prelim.

The lid sits on top of a paraboloid, which is supported by three rods jammed symmetrically in to a small cylinder.

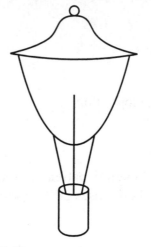

With coordinate axes taken as shown, and the trophy viewed so that one rod is on the extreme right (touching the cup, the rim of the cylinder and the centre of the base of the cylinder), the dimensions are as shown and the equation of the parabola viewed is $y = 2x^2 + 2$.

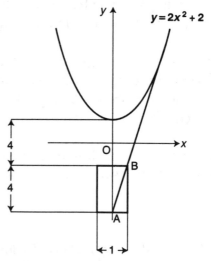

$y = 2x^2 + 2$

(a) Find the equation of the rod AB. **(4)**

(b) Show that the rod is a tangent to the parabola and find the coordinates of the point of contact. **(5)**

Total: 60 marks

[END OF QUESTION PAPER]

NATIONAL
QUALIFICATIONS
Time 1 hour 10 minutes

PRACTICE PAPER E

MATHEMATICS
HIGHER
Paper 1
(Non-calculator)

Refer to page 3 for Instructions to Candidates

All questions should be attempted

Marks

1. Differentiate $3\sqrt{x}$ with respect to x. **(2)**

2. (a) Show that the points L(1, –2, 0), M(5, –4, 4) and N(7, –5, 6) are collinear. **(3)**

   (b) Find the ratio in which M divides LN. **(1)**

3. Solve $2\sin^2 x = 1 + \sin x$ for $0 < x < 2\pi$. **(5)**

4. I feed my budgie every Sunday morning. Every week he eats 60% of whatever seed he had at the start of the week. He started off with a full feeding bottle, which contained 200 g of Chirp. When I feed him on a Sunday, I give him half of the amount of Chirp that would be needed to fill up the feeding bottle completely.

   If this feeding pattern continues indefinitely, what will be the least amount of Chirp ever in his feeding bottle? **(6)**

Marks

5. Find the range of values of x for which $2x^2 + 5x - 7 \leq 0$ $(x \in R)$. **(3)**

6. A circle of radius 5 has its centre at the point (2, 1).

    (a) Find the equation of this circle, expressing your answer without brackets. **(2)**

    (b) The line with equation $y = x - 2$ intersects the circle at the points A and B. Find the length of the cord AB. **(6)**

    (c) Write down the gradient of the line joining the centre of the circle to the mid-point of AB. **(1)**

7. If $t(x) = k \cos 2x$ and $t'\left(\dfrac{\pi}{4}\right) = 4$, find the value of k. **(4)**

Marks

8. Three vectors p, q and r are such that $p \cdot (q + r) = q \cdot (p + r)$.

Show that r must be perpendicular to $p - q$. **(3)**

9. In $\triangle ABC$, $\hat{B} = 90°$, $AB = 8$ units, $BC = 15$ units and D lies on BC such that $BD = 6$ units.

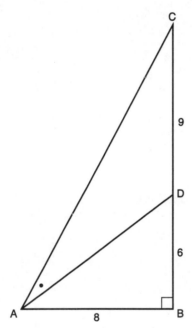

Calculate the exact value of $\sin C\hat{A}D$. **(5)**

Marks

10. *(a)* Express $2 \cos x° - 2\sqrt{3} \sin x°$ in the form $k \cos (x + a)$, where $k > 0$ and $0 < a < 360$. **(4)**

(b) Hence state the greatest and least values of this expression, and the smallest positive values of x for which they occur. **(2)**

11. Solve $\log_5 (3x + 61) - \log_5 x = 3$. **(3)**

Total: 50 marks

[END OF QUESTION PAPER]

NATIONAL
QUALIFICATIONS
Time 1 hour 30 minutes

PRACTICE PAPER E

MATHEMATICS
HIGHER
Paper 2

Refer to page 3 for Instructions to Candidates

All questions should be attempted

Marks

1. The functions f, g and h are defined on the set of real numbers by

$$f(x) = 2x + 1, \qquad g(x) = 3x^2 + 2, \qquad h(x) = \frac{x-1}{2}.$$

  (a) Find the values of
     (i) a if $f(a) = 17$, **(1)**
     (ii) b if $g(b) = 110$. **(2)**

  (b) Find, in their simplest form, formulae for
     (i) $g(f(x))$, **(3)**
     (ii) $h(f(x))$. **(3)**

  (c) One of your answers to part *(b)* should suggest a relationship between two of these three given functions. Describe this relationship. **(1)**

2. *(a)* Find the centre and radius of the circle which has equation $x^2 + y^2 - 16x - 10y + 73 = 0$. **(2)**

  (b) ABCD is a square. The sides of the square are parallel to the coordinate axes and are also tangents to the given circle.

  Find the equation of the circle which passes through A, B, C and D.

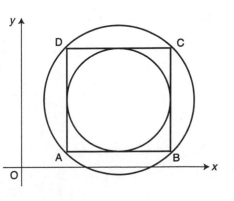

(2)

Marks

3. When $f(x) = x^3 + x^2 + px + q$ is divided by $(x-4)$ the remainder is 48. One factor of $f(x)$ is $(x-2)$.

    (a) Find the values of p and q.   **(5)**

    (b) Hence, factorise $f(x)$ completely.   **(3)**

4. Part of a flume at a swimming pool is in the shape of the cubic curve with equation $y = x^3 - 2x^2 + x + 18$.

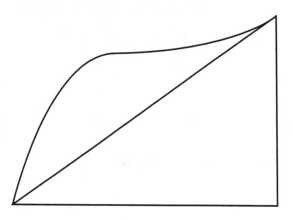

A supporting beam takes up the position of the tangent to this curve at the point where $x = 2$.

    (a) Find the equation of the beam.   **(5)**

    (b) Find the coordinates of the bottom of the beam, where it meets the flume again.   **(5)**

5. Evaluate $\displaystyle\int_{2}^{3}(2x-5)^4\,dx$ **(4)**

Marks

6. The wheel house of a river barge is in the shape of half a 2 m cube placed centrally on the deck of the barge. There is a 4 m radio beacon attached at the forward starboard corner of the wheel house, as shown.

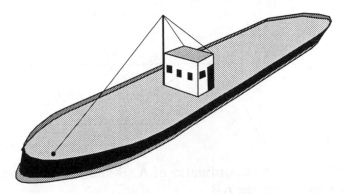

The top of the beacon is secured by a wire to the deck at a point 8 m in front of the wheel house, another wire to the near rear corner, and a strut to the opposite diagonal corner of the wheel house.

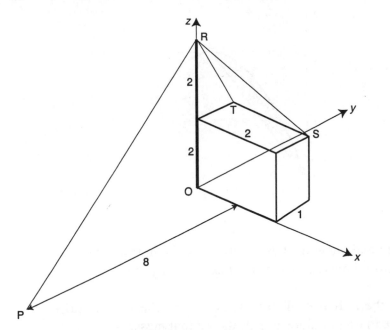

Coordinate axes are taken as shown.

(a) Write down the coordinates of P, R, S and T. **(4)**

(b) Calculate the angle between the wire RP and the strut RS. **(7)**

Marks

7. Part of the graph of $y = (x-1)^2(x-3)$ is shown.

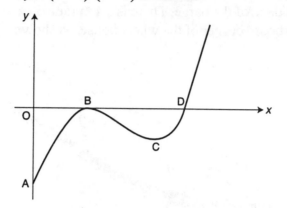

   (a) Write down the coordinates of A, B and D, and hence find the equation of the line AB. **(5)**

   (b) Calculate the area enclosed between this curve and the line AB in the diagram below.

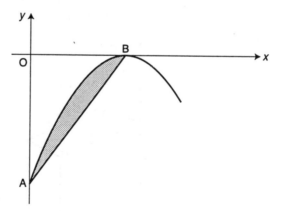

   (4)

8. A radioactive element decays according to the law $m_t = m_0 e^{-0.01\,t}$, where m_0 is the initial mass and m_t is the mass after t years.

   Calculate the half-life of this element, i.e., the time required for the radioactive mass to reduce to half its original mass. **(4)**

Total: 60 marks

[END OF QUESTION PAPER]

NATIONAL
QUALIFICATIONS
Time 1 hour 10 minutes

PRACTICE PAPER F

MATHEMATICS
HIGHER
Paper 1
(Non-calculator)

Refer to page 3 for Instructions to Candidates

All questions should be attempted

Marks

1. Find the equation of the line through the point (2, 1) and perpendicular to the line with equation $2x - y + 8 = 0$. **(3)**

2. A curve has equation $y = x^3 + 2x - 5$.

   (a) Show that this curve is increasing at every point on it. **(3)**

   (b) Find the equation of the tangent at the point where $x = -1$. **(3)**

3. Integrate $4x + 5$ with respect to x. **(2)**

4. Find the values of a and b if $(x - 2)$ and $(x + 4)$ are both factors of $x^4 + ax^3 - x^2 + bx - 8$. **(5)**

5. Given that $\tan x = \frac{3}{4}$ and $\tan y = \frac{7}{24}$, where x and y are acute angles, find the **exact** value of $\sin(2x + y)$. **(5)**

Marks

6. Make a copy of this graph of the function $y = 3^x$.

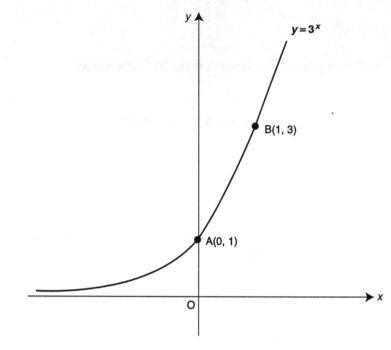

On your copy sketch the graph of $y = 1 - 3^x$, showing the images of A and B.

(4)

Marks

7. V,ABCD is a right square pyramid.

    AC and BD meet at X.

    L lies two thirds of the way up XV.

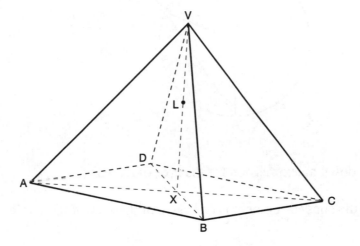

Relative to suitable axes,

$\overrightarrow{AB} = 5i + 4j + k, \quad \overrightarrow{AD} = 3i + 2j - k, \quad \overrightarrow{AV} = 13i - 9j + 3k.$

Find the components of

(a) $\overrightarrow{AX}$ (3)

(b) $\overrightarrow{XV}$ (2)

(c) $\overrightarrow{AL}$ (3)

8. Show that the circles with equations $(x - 1)^2 + (y - 2)^2 = 4$ and $(x - 6)^2 + (y - 2)^2 = 9$ touch each other, and write down the equation of the common tangent at their common point. (5)

Marks

9. A chord AB of a circle of radius r subtends an angle of θ radians at the centre of the circle, as shown.

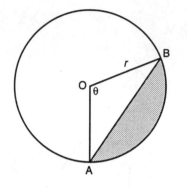

(a) Write down an expression for the area of $\triangle$OAB. **(1)**

The area of the shaded segment is one sixth of the area of the circle.

(b) Show that $\sin \theta = \theta - \frac{\pi}{3}$. **(4)**

10. Solve $\sin x - \sqrt{3} \cos x = 1$ for $0 \leq x \leq 2\pi$. **(7)**

Total: 50 marks

[END OF QUESTION PAPER]

NATIONAL
QUALIFICATIONS
Time 1 hour 30 minutes

PRACTICE PAPER F

MATHEMATICS
HIGHER
Paper 2

Refer to page 3 for Instructions to Candidates

All questions should be attempted

Marks

1. Triangle DEF has vertices D(5, 8), E(–2, 1) and F(6, –1).

    The median EM and the altitude FG meet at T.

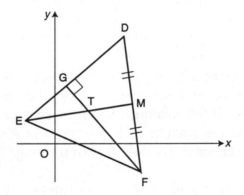

    Find *(a)* the equation of EM, **(3)**

    (b) the equation of FG, **(3)**

    (c) the coordinates of T. **(4)**

2. For what values of a does the equation $x^2 - 2ax + (a + 2) = 0$ have real roots? **(5)**

Marks

3. Find the equation of the tangent to the curve $y = \sqrt{x^2 + 5}$ at the point (2, 3). **(5)**

4. (a) Show that the triangle with vertices P(2, –4), Q(4, –6) and R(8, –2) is right angled. **(3)**

   (b) **Write down** the centre of the circle which passes through P, Q and R. **(2)**

   (c) Find the equation of the circle which passes through P, Q and R. **(2)**

   (d) Find the length of the chord which the circle makes on the *x*-axis. **(3)**

5. (a) A patient, A, is given a 250 mg dose of the drug hyproxydol every four hours. Half of the amount of hyproxydol in the body is lost every four hours. If this treatment is continued for a considerable time, show that the amount of hyproxydol in A's body never exceeds that contained in a double dose of the drug. **(4)**

   (b) Another patient, B, was given the same treatment as A except that he was given a double dose initially. What difference would this make to the amount of drug in B's body? **(2)**

   (c) It is later discovered that taking a vitamin C tablet along with the hyproxydol causes only 25% of the amount of the drug in the body to be lost every four hours. This procedure is now adopted for patient A. How does this change affect the maximum amount of hyproxydol in A's body in the long term? **(4)**

6. For $f(x) = 3 \sin 2x + 2 \cos 3x$, evaluate $f'\left(\dfrac{\pi}{6}\right)$. **(5)**

Marks

7.   *(a)*   Evaluate $\textbf{\textit{u}}.\textbf{\textit{v}}$ where $\textbf{\textit{u}} = \begin{pmatrix} 3 \\ 4 \\ -1 \end{pmatrix}$ and $\textbf{\textit{v}} = \begin{pmatrix} 3 \\ -2 \\ 1 \end{pmatrix}$.   **(1)**

   (b)   Hence, show that A(4, 4, 10), B($-2, -4$, 12) and C(-8, 0, 10) are the vertices of a right-angled triangle stating which is the right angle.   **(3)**

8.   Solve the equation $3 \cos 2x° + 2 \cos x° = 1$ for $0 \le x \le 360$.   **(6)**

9.   After an experiment involving the variables p and q, the values of $\log_e p$ were plotted against those of $\log_e q$ and the result was the straight line graph shown.

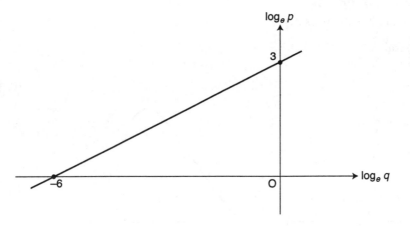

   Find the relationship between p and q.   **(5)**

Total: 60 marks

[END OF QUESTION PAPER]

ANSWERS

PRACTICE PAPER A

Paper 1

1. $2(p + 2q)$ 2.   (a) 10 (b) $\frac{2}{3}$

3.   (a) $\frac{7}{25}$ (b) $-\frac{527}{625}$

4.   (a) $(x-1)^2 + (y-2)^2 = 5$ (b) $(x-3)^2 + (y-4)^2 = 16$

5.   Proof: $\Delta = k^2 > 0$ for all k 6. $3 \sin^2 x \cos x$

7.

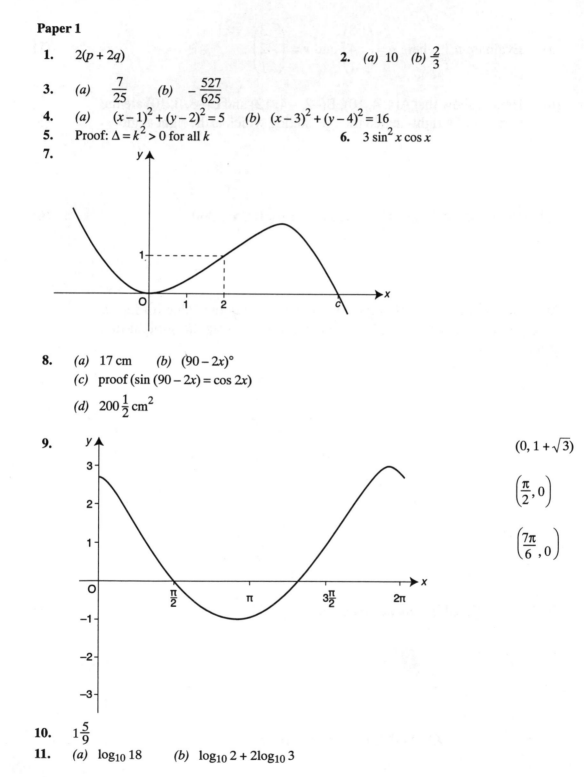

8.   (a) 17 cm   (b) $(90 - 2x)^\circ$

    (c) proof $(\sin(90 - 2x) = \cos 2x)$

    (d) $200\frac{1}{2}$ cm^2

9.

$(0, 1 + \sqrt{3})$

$\left(\frac{\pi}{2}, 0\right)$

$\left(\frac{7\pi}{6}, 0\right)$

10. $1\frac{5}{9}$

11.   (a) $\log_{10} 18$ (b) $\log_{10} 2 + 2\log_{10} 3$

Paper 2

1. -2

2. *(a)* B(8, 10, 0), D(0, 0, 6), H(4, 5, 12)   *(b)* 74·95°

3. *(a)* proof   *(b)* $y = 4x + 1$ *(c)* proof (2, 9)

4. $3 \sin (x - 48·2)°$

5. $14 \frac{7}{12}$ units^2

6. *(a)* proof   *(b)* $(x + 1)(x - 2)(x - 4)$ *(c)* $-1, 2, 4$

7. *(a)* proof   *(b)* $x = 20, y = 10$, £880   [Remember to justify the minimum.]

8. $\log_{10} y = 2 + 4\log_{10} x$

PRACTICE PAPER B

Paper 1

1. $x = 5$

2. $(x - 4)^2 + (y - 3)^2 = 25$

3. $(x + 1)(x - 2)(2x - 3)$

4. *(a)* $9 - (x - 2)^2$ *(b)* $x < -1$

5. M(2, 7, 8), $\overrightarrow{AM} = \begin{pmatrix} 1 \\ 5 \\ 5 \end{pmatrix}$

6. $2\dfrac{15}{16}$

7. *(a)*

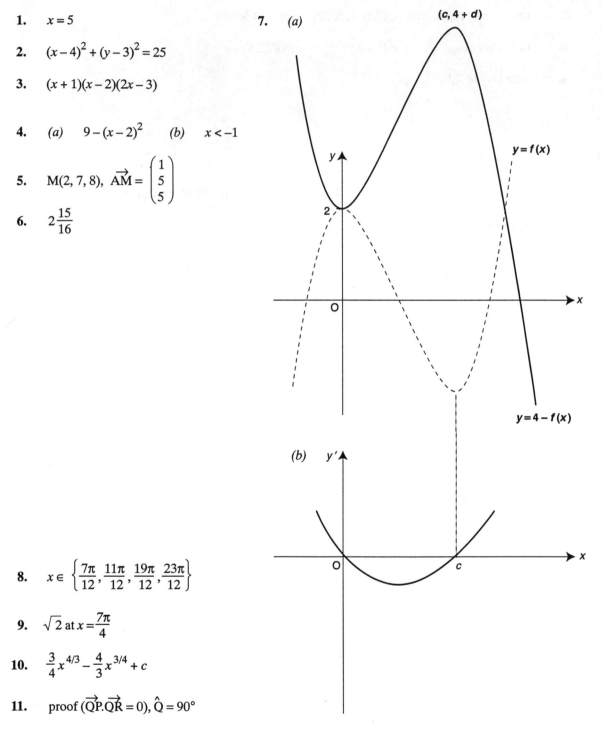

8. $x \in \left\{ \dfrac{7\pi}{12}, \dfrac{11\pi}{12}, \dfrac{19\pi}{12}, \dfrac{23\pi}{12} \right\}$

9. $\sqrt{2}$ at $x = \dfrac{7\pi}{4}$

10. $\dfrac{3}{4} x^{4/3} - \dfrac{4}{3} x^{3/4} + c$

11. proof $(\overrightarrow{QP}.\overrightarrow{QR} = 0)$, $\hat{Q} = 90°$

12. $\dfrac{2 - 3\sin x}{2\sqrt{2x + 3\cos x}}$

54

Paper 2

1.   *(a)* $12{\cdot}5, 23{\cdot}75, 40{\cdot}625$ *(b)* $u_{11} = 1287{\cdot}46\ldots$

2.   *(a)* $x + 2y = 1$ *(b)* $7y = 4x - 19$ *(c)* $(3, -1)$

3. $(5, 5), (1, 7), 2\sqrt{5}$

4.   *(a)*   proof   *(b)* $x \in \{60, 131{\cdot}8, 228{\cdot}2, 300\}$

5.   *(a)* $a = 2, b = 2, c = 2$ *(b)* $0{\cdot}912, 2{\cdot}230$

6.   *(a)* $y = 12 - \dfrac{1}{3}x$ *(b)*   proof $(3, 11)$

7.   proof $(\, p \cdot (\, p - 2q) = 0)$

8.   *(a)*   proof   *(b)* $\sqrt{3}$

9. $P = 54{\cdot}6t^{-0{\cdot}8}$

PRACTICE PAPER C

Paper 1

1. $5x + 4y = 7$ **2.**   3   **3.**   16

4.

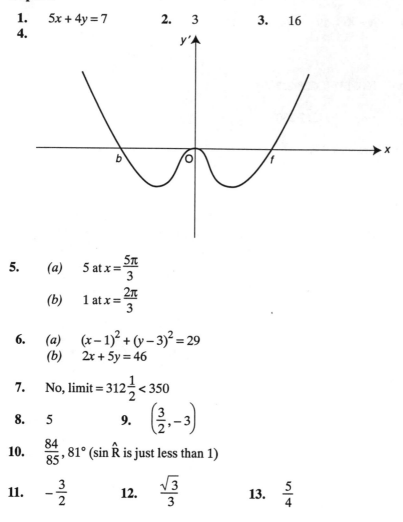

5.   *(a)* 5 at $x = \dfrac{5\pi}{3}$

      (b) 1 at $x = \dfrac{2\pi}{3}$

6.   *(a)* $(x-1)^2 + (y-3)^2 = 29$
      (b) $2x + 5y = 46$

7.   No, limit $= 312\dfrac{1}{2} < 350$

8.   5   **9.** $\left(\dfrac{3}{2}, -3\right)$

10. $\dfrac{84}{85}$, $81°$ ($\sin \hat{R}$ is just less than 1)

11. $-\dfrac{3}{2}$ **12.** $\dfrac{\sqrt{3}}{3}$ **13.** $\dfrac{5}{4}$

Paper 2

1. $15(3x + 4)^4$

2. (a) $\sin^2 x$ (b) $2x^2 - x^4$

3. $21 \cdot 8°$

4. $x \in \{-1, 2, 3\}$

5. $2\pi + 10\frac{2}{3}$

6. (a) proof (check **three** scalar products) (b) $36 \cdot 7°$

7. (a) $y = 4x + 5$ (b) $(-2, -3)$

8.

9. (a) proof

   (b) $35\frac{5}{6}\left(\text{when } x = \frac{5}{3}\right)$

10. maximum 30 at $x = 136 \cdot 4°$
    minimum -28 at $x = 316 \cdot 4°$

Paper 1

1. $5y = 2x - 16$

2. $y = 2x + 2$

3. $(x - 5)^2 + (y - 2)^2 = 25$

4. $10 - (x + 3)^2$

5. (a) $\begin{pmatrix} -5 \\ 3 \\ 1 \end{pmatrix}$ (b) $\begin{pmatrix} 5 \\ 5 \\ 10 \end{pmatrix}$ (c) $\begin{pmatrix} -1 \\ 7 \\ 9 \end{pmatrix}$

6. $\dfrac{1}{4}$

7. (a)

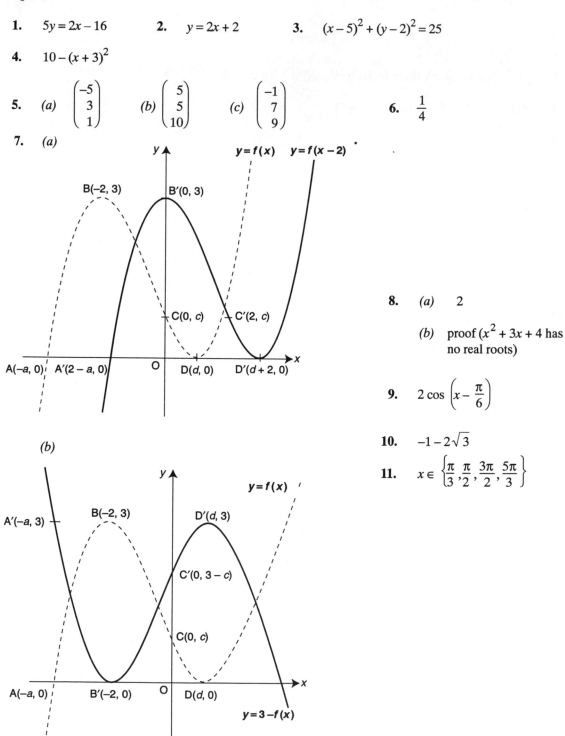

8. (a) 2

   (b) proof ($x^2 + 3x + 4$ has no real roots)

9. $2 \cos \left(x - \dfrac{\pi}{6} \right)$

10. $-1 - 2\sqrt{3}$

11. $x \in \left\{ \dfrac{\pi}{3}, \dfrac{\pi}{2}, \dfrac{3\pi}{2}, \dfrac{5\pi}{3} \right\}$

Paper 2

1.   *(a)* $3y = 4x - 7$ *(b)* $2y = x + 2$ *(c)* $(4, 3)$

2. $(-3, 3)$, 9 3. $5\frac{1}{3}$

4.   *(a)*   A$(8, 0, 0)$, C$(0, 12, 0)$,   *(b)*   P$(2, 9, 5)$, Q$(6, 3, 5)$ *(c)* $43 \cdot 2°$

5. $x \in \{0, 138\cdot6, 180, 221\cdot4, 360\}$

6. $-2x^{-1/2} + c$ 7. $\log_a 3a^2$

8.   *(a)*   proof $(0\cdot8^4 \doteqdot 0\cdot41)$ *(b)*   3   *(c)*   safe (limit $\doteqdot 420 < 500$)

9. $p = 3q^4$

10.   *(a)* $y = 8x - 6$ *(b)* $(2, 10)$

PRACTICE PAPER E

Paper 1

1. $\frac{3}{2}x^{-1/2}$

2. *(a)* proof (including 'parallel lines' **and** 'common point')　　*(b)* 2:1

3. $x \in \left\{ \dfrac{\pi}{2}, \dfrac{7\pi}{6}, \dfrac{11\pi}{6} \right\}$

4. $50\,g$ $\left(\text{use } u_{n+1} = 0{\cdot}4\left[u_n + 100 - \dfrac{1}{2}u_n \right] \text{ or } u_{n+1} = 0{\cdot}4 \times \dfrac{1}{2} \times (u_n + 200) \text{ and simplify} \right)$

5. $\dfrac{-7}{2} \le x \le 1$

6. *(a)* $x^2 + y^2 - 4x - 2y - 20 = 0$　　*(b)* $(-1, -3), (6, 4), 7\sqrt{2}$　　*(c)* -1

7. -2

8. proof $(\boldsymbol{r} \cdot (\boldsymbol{p} - \boldsymbol{q}) = 0)$

9. $\dfrac{36}{85}$ (use $\sin(\hat{CAB} - \hat{DAB})$)

10. *(a)* $4\cos(x + 60)°$　　*(b)* 4 maximum at $x = 300$　　-4 minimum at $x = 120$

11. $\dfrac{1}{2}$

Paper 2

1. *(a)* (i) 8 (ii) ±6 *(b)* (i) $12x^2 + 12x + 5$ (ii) x *(c)* h and f are inverses of each other

2. *(a)* (8, 5), 4 *(b)* $(x-8)^2 + (y-5)^2 = 32$

3. $p = -10$, $q = 8$, $f(x) = (x-1)(x-2)(x+4)$

4. *(a)* $y = 5x + 10$ *(b)* (−2, 0)

5. $\dfrac{1}{5}$

6. *(a)* P(1, −8, 0), R(0, 0, 4), S(2, 1, 2), T(0, 1, 2) *(b)* 85·8°

7. *(a)* A(0, −3), B(1, 0), C(3, 0), $y = 3x - 3$ *(b)* $\dfrac{7}{12}$ units^2

8. 69 years 4 months (approx)

PRACTICE PAPER F

Paper 1

1. $x + 2y = 4$

2. *(a)* proof $(3x^2 + 2 > 0$ for all $x)$ *(b)* $y = 5x - 3$

3. $2x^2 + 5x + c$

4. $a = 5, b = -22$

5. 1

6.
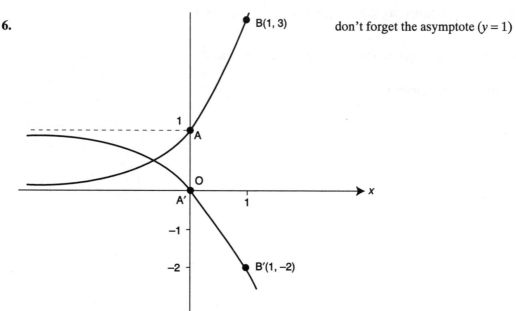

don't forget the asymptote $(y = 1)$

7. *(a)* $\begin{pmatrix} 4 \\ 3 \\ 0 \end{pmatrix}$ *(b)* $\begin{pmatrix} 9 \\ -12 \\ 3 \end{pmatrix}$ *(c)* $\begin{pmatrix} 10 \\ -5 \\ 2 \end{pmatrix}$

8. proof (distance between centres equals sum of radii); $x = 3$

9. *(a)* $\frac{1}{2}r^2 \sin\theta$ *(b)* proof

10. $x \in \left\{\dfrac{\pi}{2}, \dfrac{7\pi}{6}\right\}$ (use the auxiliary angle)

Paper 2

1. (a) $3y = x + 5$ (b) $x + y = 5$ (c) $\left(\dfrac{5}{2}, \dfrac{5}{2}\right)$

2. $\{a \leq -1\} \cup \{a \geq 2\}$

3. $3y = 2x + 5$

4. (a) proof (use $m_1 . m_2 = -1$) (b) $(5, -3)$ (mid-point of hypotenuse)
   (c) $(x - 5)^2 + (y + 3)^2 = 10$ (d) 2

5. (a) proof (limit = 500) (b) each dose tops him up to 500 mg
   (c) it is doubled

6. -3

7. (a) 0 (b) proof $(A\hat{B}C)$

8. $x \in \{48{\cdot}2, 180, 311{\cdot}8\}$

9. $p = 20{\cdot}1\sqrt{q}$

QUESTION FREQUENCY CHART

H Maths Practice Papers	A1	A2	B1	B2	C1	C2	D1	D2	E1	E2	F1	F2
1.1 the straight line	1		1	2	1		1	1			1	1
1.2 composition of functions		6				2				1		
1.2 graphs, related graphs (inc. f')	7		7	5	4	8	7				6	
1.2 completing the square			4				4					
1.2 radians	9				5				3		9	
1.2 3D trig						3						
1.3 basic differentiation	6		6					1			2	
1.3 equation of tangent						7	2			4	2	3
1.3 stationary pts & optimization		7		8	9							
1.4 recurrence relations	2			1	7			8	4			5
2.1 remainder theorem		6	3			4	8			3	4	
2.1 quadratic theory (Δ)	5						8					2
2.1 Δ for tangency		3		6	9	7		10				
2.1 quadratic inequalities								5				
2.2 basic integration			10					6			3	
2.2 area under a curve					5			3				
2.2 area between two curves		5								7		
2.3 (A + B) trigonometry	8				10				9		5	
2.3 (2A) trigonometry	3			4			11	5			5	8
2.3 trig equations			8	4			11	5	3			8
2.4 equations of the circle	4		2	3	6		3	6		2		4
2.4 finding centre and radius								2		2		
2.4 tangents		3			6							
2.4 touching circles											8	
3.1 basic vectors		1	5		2		5	4		6	7	
3.1 collinearity								2				
3.1 scalar product (+ perpr)			11	7	3	6		8				7
3.1 angle between two vectors		2				6		4		6		
3.2 trig differentiation			12				10	7				6
3.2 trig integration					12		6					
3.2 chain rule (brackets)			12		11	1						3
3.2 integration of $f(ax + b)$	10									5		
3.3 laws of logs	11				8,13			7	11			
3.3 growth and decay										8		
3.3 experimental data		8		9				9				9
3.4 $a \cos x + b \sin x$		4	9			10	9		10			
3.4 equations: $a \cos x + b \sin x = c$											10	

Printed by Bell & Bain Ltd., Glasgow, Scotland, U.K.